Mrs. Wiggles
NUMBERS

Lisa Konkol

In a schoolhouse far away,
magic blew the fields of hay.

Mrs. Wiggles stood alone. Long ago, her class had grown. Then one day, she heard a sound . . .

Numbers leaping to the ground.

Mrs. Wiggles clapped with glee,
"Welcome students, come join me!
Time for roll-call and a game.
Stand up tall and state your name."

"I am One, amazing me!"

"I am Two, but need to pee."

“I am Three and crave a crowd.”

"I am Four and booming loud."

"I am Five, fantastic fun."

"I am Six, the fastest one."

"I am Seven and polite."

"I am Eight and blazing bright."

“I am Nine, a sleepy head.”

“Wake up students,” teacher said.

"Form a line and get a snack."

Then a squeak came from the back . . .

"Wait. I'm Zero. I can't count.
I'm worth nothing — no amount."

“Hmm,” the students thought a bit...
One then yelled, “I know — you fit!”

"Stand by me. I'll share my might.
We are ten, and you're alright."

"Be my friend," called number Two.
"I am twenty, next to you."

"No crowd here. Let's sing a song.
Number thirty gets along."

“We make forty and s’mores!
Friends forever, I am yours!”

Five then hollered, "Ride with me.
We are fifty, feeling free!"

"We look better than before.
All together, we are more!"

"Start with Zero, end with Nine . . .

. . . side by side we brightly shine!"

In the schoolhouse beyond the grass,
Mrs. Wiggles loves her class.

Count the Items

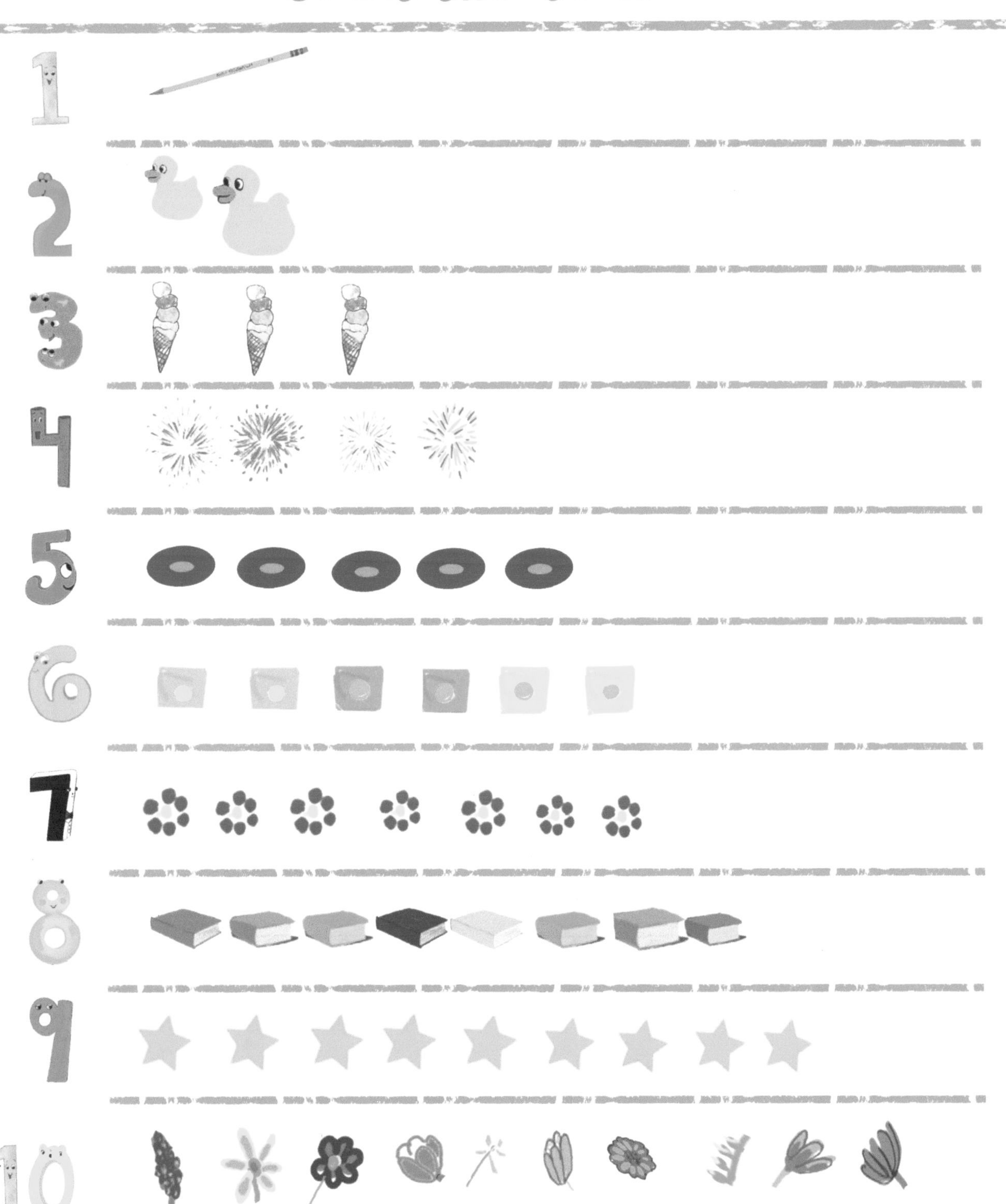

For Elizabeth, Emily, and Tom

Mrs. Wiggles and the Numbers

Softcover: ISBN 978-1-7359196-3-8
Hardcover: ISBN 978-1-7359196-2-1

Published in 2023 by Baa Baa Books, LLC
First Edition. February 2023, 32 pages, 7.5" x 9.25"

Thank you Steve

Scan the code for more activity sheets and fun!
www.lisakonkol.com